Autumn
SPY IT! SCORE IT!

Introduction

Autumn is the season between summer and winter, and in the UK, it spans the entire months of September, October and November. With temperatures starting to drop, leaves begin to fall from trees, animals start their preparations for staying warm and well-fed over winter, and some birds start their migrations in search of a different climate.

But it's not just nature that marks the changing of the seasons... There are many cultural festivals celebrated in the autumn months, like Halloween and Bonfire Night. Not to mention the warming food and drink we begin to fill up on, and the cosy clothing that we dig out to keep ourselves warm and dry.

So, wherever you are, and whatever you're up to, get spotting all things autumn!

How to use your i-SPY book

Keep your eyes peeled for the i-SPYs in the book.

If you spy it, score it by ticking the circle or star.

50 POINTS

Items with a star are difficult to spot so you'll have to search high and low to find them.

Once you score 1000 points, send away for your super i-SPY certificate. Follow the instructions on page 64 to find out how.

Colours of autumn

Autumn is a colourful month, especially for reds, oranges and yellows. See what other colours you can find too.

Red berries

10 POINTS

You won't have to look far to find red berries in autumn because so many shrubs and trees produce them. Leave them for the birds to eat though, because some of them are poisonous to humans.

Orange pumpkins

15 POINTS

Pumpkins grow on the ground on long, creeping stems, and ripen in October and November. They are easy to grow and if there are any left over after Halloween, use them to make a delicious pumpkin pie! If you can't find them growing on the ground, look for them in a supermarket.

Yellow leaves

Deciduous trees lose their leaves in the autumn, but not before they have put on a beautiful display of colour. Look out for yellow leaves on trees such as hazel, silver birch and field maple.

20 POINTS

3

Colours of autumn

Purple Michaelmas daisies

You will often see these pretty flowers growing in gardens and parks around Michaelmas Day, which is on 29th September.

20 POINTS

Blue sky

It's lovely to go for a walk on a crisp, autumn day when the sun is shining, the sky is blue and there's a nip in the air. Wrap up warm!

5 POINTS

Green conker case

Look out for round, green, spiky seed cases growing on horse chestnut trees in early September. When a seed case falls to the ground, it splits open to reveal a shiny conker.

10 POINTS

Weather

Autumn marks the change from summer to winter. There is lots of different weather to look out for and fun weather activities to do!

Dew

As the nights start to get colder, you will often see tiny droplets of water on blades of grass the next morning. This is called dew.

Drizzle

Drizzle often falls in autumn. It is very fine, light rain, but if you are out in it for long enough, you will still get wet.

Mist

Mist is made up of lots of tiny water droplets, which hang in a cloud close to the ground. If mist becomes really dense, it's known as fog, and it can make it very difficult to see where you're going.

35 POINTS

Heavy rain

If the rain is heavy, you definitely need your raincoat!

 5 POINTS

Jump in a puddle

After the rain has cleared, the best thing to do is put your wellies on and jump in a puddle!

 10 POINTS

Mud

When rain falls onto bare soil the result is wonderfully, squelchy mud.

 5 POINTS

Hail

When raindrops freeze high up in the sky, they fall to the ground as litle balls of ice called hailstones. Hail showers can be very heavy, but they don't usually last long.

30 POINTS

Strong wind

10 POINTS

Autumn can be a stormy season, with strong winds blowing in off the sea. It's what helps the leaves to fall from the trees.

Fallen leaves

It's fun to kick through piles of leaves on the ground, though they can get very slippery when they're wet.

5 POINTS

Clothing

All this different weather means needing to wear clothes that will keep you warm and dry.

Jumper

Jumpers can be made of wool, cotton or fleece. They help keep us warm.

5 POINTS

Gloves

Gloves are a must for keeping your hands warm when you're out for a walk in late autumn.

5 POINTS

Woolly socks

A pair of thick woolly socks is the best way to help keep toes cosy as the weather gets colder.

5 POINTS

Clothing

Wellies

Splashing in puddles and squelching through mud are much easier in a pair of wellies. How many different colours can you spot?

Umbrella

An umbrella will keep your head and shoulders dry during autumn showers. Many are plain, but some are more fun and come in bright colours and animal designs.

Hat

Hats come in all shapes and sizes, but it's a woolly or fleecy one that you are most likely to see in the autumn.

Scarf

Scarves keep your neck warm when it's cold and windy. If you don't have one, you could learn to knit one yourself!

5 POINTS

Raincoat

Raincoats come in all sorts of colours and patterns, and help to protect us from wind and rain.

5 POINTS

Night sky

As the dark nights draw in, you have more opportunity to observe the night sky. Some of the things you'll see are only visible at this time of year because of the way the Earth is moving through space.

Polaris (the North Star)

Polaris isn't the brightest star in the sky but it is one of the easiest to spot, so for centuries it was used by sailors to work out where they were going. The whole northern sky revolves around this star.

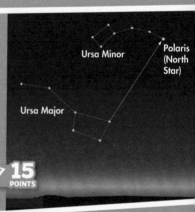

Ursa Minor

Polaris (North Star)

Ursa Major

15 POINTS

Sirius

This is the brightest star in the sky. It is also known as the Dog Star, because it's the chief star in the constellation Canis Major, or the Big Dog.

Sirius

15 POINTS

The Plough

10 POINTS

Seven stars make up the most recognisable pattern in the night sky. If you join the dots, they make the shape of a traditional plough or saucepan. The Plough isn't a constellation, but a group of stars called an asterism within the larger constellation of Ursa Major.

Ursa Minor

This constellation is also called the Little Bear. It contains Polaris and six other stars which make a similar shape to The Plough, but higher up in the sky.

15 POINTS

Pegasus

This constellation is named after the winged horse in Greek mythology, and is almost directly overhead. The easiest part to spot is the square shape made by four of its stars.

20 POINTS

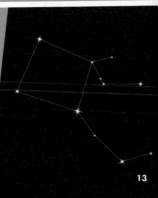

Night sky

Andromeda

Andromeda is right next to Pegasus. In fact they share a star! There are fifteen other stars in this constellation, which is named after a mythical princess.

35 POINTS

Capricornus

This is one of the constellations of the zodiac and can be seen in early autumn, on the opposite side of the sky to The Plough. It represents a goat.

15 POINTS

Aries

Aries the ram is best seen in November. It is made up of four stars joined together in a line, lower down in the sky from Andromeda.

15 POINTS

Pisces

This constellation covers a lot of sky between Aries and Pegasus. The two fish from this zodiac sign are joined by a long V-shaped cord.

15 POINTS

Orionid meteor shower

Watch out for 'shooting stars' as planet Earth travels through the debris left behind by Halley's Comet. The Orionid meteor shower has some of the fastest and brightest meteors. It peaks in late October, but you'll have to get up early because the best time to see it is just before dawn.

50 POINTS

Night sky

International Space Station (ISS)

The ISS is the second brightest object in the night sky, after the Moon, and looks like a bright light moving quickly across the sky from west to east. It orbits the Earth in just over 1½ hours, and is easiest to spot at dusk and dawn.

20 POINTS

Harvest Moon

The Full Moon in September is known as the Harvest Moon. This is because it's very bright and rises early, traditionally helping farmers to harvest their crops into the night.

15 POINTS

Trees and their leaves

Autumn is also known as 'fall' because it's when the leaves fall from the trees to the ground. See this for yourself by looking for these trees and their leaves.

English oak

20 POINTS

The English oak is the second most common tree in the UK and can live for hundreds of years. The leaves have wavy edges and turn brown in the autumn.

Beech

Beech leaves turn a beautiful copper colour in the autumn. As winter approaches, you might still find a few of them clinging to the branches of beech trees and hedges.

15 POINTS

Trees and their leaves

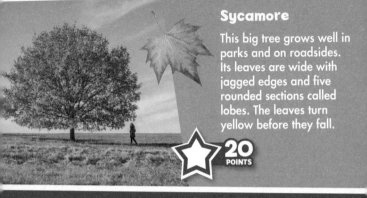

Sycamore

This big tree grows well in parks and on roadsides. Its leaves are wide with jagged edges and five rounded sections called lobes. The leaves turn yellow before they fall.

20 POINTS

Horse chestnut

This is another big tree that you might find in a park or along the pavement. Its leaves are described as 'palmate' because they look like a hand with five or more long fingers. They turn orange-yellow in the autumn.

20 POINTS

Silver birch

Look out for this tall tree in gardens and woodland all over the UK. It gets its name from the silvery bark on its trunk. The small triangle-shaped leaves turn yellow in the autumn, and flutter in the wind.

20 POINTS

Rowan

Rowan is a medium-sized tree which used to be planted beside houses to keep witches away. Its leaves are like feathers, with separate sections called 'leaflets', which turn yellow and orange.

20 POINTS

Trees and their leaves

30 POINTS

Japanese maple

This small tree puts on a spectacular display of colour in the autumn. It is often grown in pots in gardens, but can grow in the ground too.

10 POINTS

Catch a falling leaf

Wait for a windy day and try to catch a leaf as it falls from the tree.

Seeds

Seeds come in all shapes and sizes. They are produced by trees and plants and get carried around by birds, animals, insects and the wind. When they land on the ground, they grow into new trees or plants.

Acorn

Acorns are the seeds of the oak tree. Don't look for them on a young tree because they don't start growing until the tree is 40 years old. The smooth, oval seed sits in a little cup which is attached to the branch.

20 POINTS

Conker

You will find brown shiny conkers on the ground around horse chestnut trees. In the past they were used to treat horses with coughs, which is how the tree got its name.

10 POINTS

Seeds

Sycamore seed

These seeds grow in pairs on sycamore trees. They have wings and when they fall, they whirl around like helicopters.

10 POINTS

Beech mast

Beech masts are also known as beech nuts. They grow on beech trees and are a tasty treat for squirrels, mice and badgers.

20 POINTS

Pine cone

The seeds of the pine tree are hidden between the prongs that make up the cones. These prongs are called scales, and they open up in hot dry weather to let the seeds fall out.

10 POINTS

Berries

Some trees and plants produce their seeds within colourful berries. Although these are eaten by birds and small animals, many of them are poisonous to humans so you must not eat them.

Yew seed

The yew seed grows in the centre of a red berry. Don't eat them as the seeds are poisonous. You will often find yew growing as a hedge or in a churchyard.

35 POINTS

Rowan berries

The bright red or orange berries of the rowan tree grow in big bunches. Rowan trees are common on pavements and in gardens.

10 POINTS

Berries

Holly berries

You will find these bright red berries at the very end of autumn. Not all holly bushes produce berries – bushes are either male or female, and it is only the female plants that have berries.

20 POINTS

Sloes

These large, dark, round berries grow on the branches of blackthorn bushes in late autumn. You may find these bushes growing as a hedge around a farmer's field.

40 POINTS

TOP SPOT!

Pyracantha berries

Pyracantha is a shrub that is usually found in gardens, growing against a wall or as a hedge. It has masses of bright red, orange or yellow berries.

25 POINTS

Elderberries

These tiny purple-black berries grow in bunches on elder trees, which you will find growing in gardens, woods and along country lanes. Look for them in September and October.

30 POINTS

Hawthorn berries

Hawthorn is a small tree that often grows in hedgerows and is great for wildlife. Small animals such as dormice love to eat the small red berries, which are called haws.

30 POINTS

Rosehips

Rosehips are the fruit of rose plants, and grow on the flower stem once the flower has died. You will find these plants in parks and gardens, and also growing in the wild.

15 POINTS

Fungi

Autumn is the best season to find a wide variety of fungi growing in woodlands, parks and gardens. Be very careful not to touch or eat them, as some are very poisonous.

Oyster mushroom

These flat, light-coloured mushrooms grow in clusters on the trunks of deciduous trees like beech. They can be up to 25 cm across. They are carnivorous, and like to eat nematode worms!

35 POINTS

Chicken of the woods

This grows in tiers of bright yellow crinkly fans on the trunks of trees; mainly oak but also willow, sweet chestnut and yew. The flesh looks a bit like chicken meat and is eaten by deer.

35 POINTS

50
POINTS

Giant puffball

These large mushrooms aren't very common. If you see one from a distance, you might think it's a football or even a small sheep! They grow in fields, meadows and lawns, often near stinging nettles.

TOP
SPOT!

27

Fungi

Chanterelle

These orange mushrooms grow in the ground in forests and woods across the country. **35 POINTS**

Shaggy inkcap

These tall, slim mushrooms are common on lawns, flower beds and roadsides. They are light in colour but produce a black ink which was used for writing with in the past. **25 POINTS**

Jelly ear

You can probably guess how this fungus got its name – it looks just like a squashed jelly ear! It grows all over the UK on tree trunks, especially elder, beech and sycamore. **30 POINTS**

Seasonal fruits and vegetables

These foods can usually be bought from shops all year round, but autumn is the time that they are harvested in the UK. Score double points if you see any of them growing in a garden, allotment or field.

Butternut squash

15 POINTS

You are more likely to find these in a shop than growing on the ground. Although they are savoury, they are actually fruits, and have seeds inside them.

Leek

Leeks are part of the onion family. You might see them growing in rows in the ground from late summer until winter.

10 POINTS

Apple

5 POINTS

Apples grow on trees, which you might see in a garden or grouped together in an orchard. There are lots of different types and they can be red, green, yellow or a mix of these colours.

Seasonal fruits and vegetables

Pear

You will find these bell-shaped fruits growing on trees in September and October, though they are not as common as apples. They are usually green or yellow-green in colour.

5 POINTS

Brussels sprouts

These miniature cabbages grow on wide stalks which grow up from the ground. They are harvested from September onwards. Not everyone likes to eat them, but they are very good for you!

10 POINTS

Parsnip

10 POINTS

Parsnips are a root vegetable, which means they grow underground. This makes them difficult to spot in a field! They look like wide, creamy-coloured carrots and have a nutty flavour.

Blackberry

You will often find blackberries growing on brambles beside a path or in a wood in early autumn. It's fun to forage for them, but only eat one if you are certain it's a blackberry, as some types of berry are poisonous.

10 POINTS

Plum/Damson

These fruits are oval-shaped and grow on small trees in early autumn. Their colour can range from deep purple, to red to yellow. They have a large seed in the middle called a stone or pit.

15 POINTS

Wildlife

As the leaves of garden flowers and plants start to die back, it can be easier to spot wildlife.

Spider

These eight-legged creatures aren't insects, but arachnids. You often see them around the house and garden.

5 POINTS

Moth

There are 2,500 species of moth in the UK. The best way to spot them is to leave a window open in the evening when it's dark outside, and moths will be attracted inside towards the light.

5 POINTS

Daddy long legs

These insects are a type of crane fly and have long, gangly legs. They fly into the house in early autumn evenings, attracted by the light.

5 POINTS

Ladybird

Ladybirds are usually found on their own in summer, but in autumn they start to huddle up in groups around window frames, in the hope of surviving the winter.

10 POINTS

33

Red-green carpet moth

These moths can be found in woods all around the country during September and October, but they are very well camouflaged!

 40 POINTS

TOP SPOT!

Peacock butterfly

The striking peacock butterfly is a common sight in gardens in early autumn. The 'eyes' on the wings help to scare predators away.

 15 POINTS

Jay

These woodland birds have a patch of electric blue feathers on their wings. Despite being shy, they are also very noisy, and spend the autumn hiding acorns in the ground to feast on during winter.

40 POINTS

TOP SPOT!

Fox

Foxes are becoming a much more common sight in towns and cities. You are most likely to see one at dusk, looking for food. Foxes aren't too fussy about what they eat! Look out for their tracks and greyish droppings.

30 POINTS

Badger

Badgers are a rare sight because they are nocturnal and live in underground tunnels. Although they live in family groups, you're more likely to see one on its own. They mainly eat earthworms, but also a wide variety of other things like berries, acorns, small mammals and even hedgehogs.

TOP SPOT!

50 POINTS

Hedgehog

Hedgehogs hibernate in nests of leaves or logs called a 'hibernaculum' from November onwards. Hedgehog numbers are declining, but you could help by making a hedgehog hibernaculum out of wood and dry leaves.

30 POINTS

Wildlife

Barn owl

You might see a barn owl at dusk near farmland, hunting for mice, voles and shrews. Their white, heart-shaped faces and fronts, and light brown backs and wings, make them easy to recognise.

TOP SPOT!

40 POINTS

Make a bird feeder

Make a bird feeder by mixing melted lard with bird seed and putting it in an empty yoghurt pot or coconut shell to set. If you add string, you can hang it in a tree for the birds to find.

15 POINTS

Animal behaviours

Autumn can be a busy time for animals, preparing for winter or getting ready to breed. Be patient if you want to spot some of these behaviours in the wild.

Grey seal coming ashore

These adorable sea creatures come ashore in the autumn to give birth to their young. After only 2 or 3 weeks, the pups are left to fend for themselves.

50 POINTS

Leaping salmon

During the autumn, these sea fish return to the rivers where they were born, to breed. As they swim against the flow of the river, they leap out of the rushing water in order to clear waterfalls and weirs.

40 POINTS

Fighting deer

Male red deer fight by locking antlers and pushing against each other, to win the right to breed with the females of the herd. This usually happens at dawn, but can go on all day.

50 POINTS

TOP SPOT!

Squirrel hiding nuts

Squirrels hide thousands of nuts in the autumn so they have enough food in the winter. Native red squirrels are much rarer than grey squirrels.

15 POINTS

Field mouse collecting food

Field mice (also called wood mice) are busy little creatures, scurrying around trying to collect food before they are seen by predators. They hide berries and seeds for the winter; any that they don't find again grow into new plants.

TOP SPOT!

40 POINTS

Migrating birds

These birds fly from one country to another to spend the winter there. Look out for them either arriving in the UK or leaving during autumn.

Pink-footed goose

From September onwards, thousands of these geese arrive in the UK from colder countries to spend the winter on farmland and wetlands. They fly in large groups arranged in a V shape.

35 POINTS

Swallow

Look out for the last few swallows as they leave in September after spending the summer in the UK. The male is easier to spot with its red throat.

15 POINTS

TOP SPOT!

Short-eared owl

This is the owl you are most likely to see during the day. It has bright yellow eyes. Although some short-eared owls stay in the UK all year, many more arrive to spend the winter there.

40 POINTS

Redwing

You can tell a redwing from a song thrush by the red patch on its side and cream stripe above the eye. Look for these birds in fields, hedgerows and woodland from October onwards.

30 POINTS

Brent goose

These small, dark geese arrive in the UK in large flocks in October. They spend the winter eating seaweed around the coast.

TOP SPOT!

40 POINTS

Wigeon

You can usually hear wigeon before you see them because of their distinctive, shrill cheep. The males have a yellow forehead. They spend the winter in the UK.

35 POINTS

Whooper swan

This swan arrives in the UK in October, making the journey from Iceland in a single day. Look out for the large yellow triangle on its bill, and listen for the *whoop whoop* sound it makes.

TOP SPOT!

40 POINTS

Bewick's swan

This swan also spends winter in the UK. It is smaller and less common than the whooper swan, and the yellow patch on its bill is more irregular in shape.

TOP SPOT!

50 POINTS

Festivals, traditions and culture

There are lots of events, sights and activities you can join in with during the autumn.

Light show

Some towns and cities have light shows in autumn, to make the most of the darker evenings. The most famous one is Blackpool Illuminations, but score points for any light display you see in a town centre.

35 POINTS

Diwali

This festival of lights is celebrated by people of Hindu, Jain and Sikh faiths with lanterns, candles and fireworks. Many city centres have organised events with music and dancing. Score if you spot decorations or lanterns in houses or shops.

TOP SPOT!

40 POINTS

46

Heritage Open Day

Every year in September, you can visit, for free, many interesting buildings that are usually closed to the public. If there isn't an event near you, visit a museum and learn more about your local heritage.

20 POINTS

Food festival

If you'd like to try some local produce, or maybe have a go at some fun food activities, visit a food festival. Score for spotting or visiting any organised festival that sells locally produced food or drink.

20 POINTS

Festivals, traditions and culture

Quirky competition

Around the country there are all sorts of weird and wonderful competitions taking place, including gurning, stone skimming, tossing the caber, musical fireworks, porridge making and conker championships. See if you can spot one near you.

40 POINTS

TOP SPOT!

Running race

Marathons and half marathons are long-distance races, but some running events have shorter races that you could take part in. Score points for either spectating or taking part.

25 POINTS

Remembrance poppy

People wear red poppies around 11th November to remember those who fought during the World Wars.

5 POINTS

Festivals, traditions and culture: Harvest

The successful bringing in of the corn was traditionally a big cause for celebration and giving thanks, because it meant that people had enough food for the coming year.

Harvest display

Nowadays food displays are made at school or a church, and it is then donated to charity.

20 POINTS

Hay bale

Hay is dried grass that is fed to cows and horses during winter. It is cut and gathered into large bundles called bales, which you will see lying in fields in September.

20 POINTS

Corn dolly

These were traditionally made out of the last sheaf of corn that was harvested, and kept until spring to ensure a good harvest the following year. If you can't find one, you could make one yourself!

TOP SPOT!

40 POINTS

Sukkah

During the Jewish harvest festival of Sukkot, meals are eaten in a special hut called a sukkah, which has branches on the roof and is decorated with fruit.

50 POINTS

TOP SPOT!

Festivals, traditions and culture: Halloween

Halloween is celebrated on 31st October with food, games and ghoulish costumes.

Carved pumpkin

It wouldn't be Halloween without a carved pumpkin. With a candle flickering inside, these can look really spooky!

5 POINTS

Trick or treaters

If your doorbell rings and you find a group of children on your doorstep saying 'Trick or treat?', it's best to give them a treat of some sweets! Score for spotting them, or for going trick or treating yourself.

5 POINTS

Apple bobbing

This traditional Halloween game involves floating some apples in a basin of water and trying to take a bite out of one without using your hands. It's not as easy as it sounds!

5 POINTS

Score 5 points for spotting each of the popular Halloween costumes you see someone wearing.

Witch costume

5 POINTS

Ghost costume

5 POINTS

Skeleton costume

5 POINTS

Wizard costume

5 POINTS

Black cat costume

5 POINTS

Werewolf costume

5 POINTS

Festivals, traditions and culture: Bonfire Night

On 5th November the night sky is lit up with fireworks and bonfires as people celebrate a failed attempt to blow up the Houses of Parliament over 400 years ago.

Bonfire

If you go to an organised event on Bonfire Night, there will probably be a huge bonfire blazing away.

20 POINTS

Sparkler

You can hold sparklers in your hand as they sizzle with bright sparks. Try writing your name in the air with one, but take care while you do it.

Palm tree firework

These are called palm tree fireworks, because they fan out from the centre like thick palm leaves.

Festivals, traditions and culture: Bonfire Night

Chrysanthemum firework

These fireworks create a burst of tailed stars that look like a round chrysanthemum flower.

10 POINTS

Willow firework

These spectacular fireworks erupt high up in the sky and create long trails that gently fall almost to the ground. They look like weeping willow trees.

Fish firework

Wriggling flurries of stars that shoot out in different directions are known as fish fireworks. They can be very colourful.

Comet firework

Comet fireworks are like shooting stars that fly up into the air, leaving a trail of sparkles behind them.

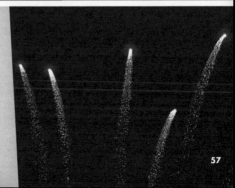

57

Food and drink

Having warm, comforting foods and drinks helps us to get used to the colder weather. Some foods are traditionally eaten at certain autumn festivals.

Harvest bread

You might find this traditional harvest bread, in the shape of a wheat sheaf, in a bakery window or a harvest festival display.

25 POINTS

Hot chocolate

There is nothing better than a mug of hot chocolate with marshmallows after you've been outside in the cold.

5 POINTS

Toffee apple

Apples dipped in toffee are a delicious treat. If you make them yourself, you can add your choice of sprinkles.

Food and drink

Honeycomb

This crunchy toffee has different names around the world, including cinder toffee, sea foam, puff candy and hokey pokey.

 15 POINTS

Soup

Soup can be made out of almost any meat or vegetable. It is always delicious with some bread and butter to dunk in it!

 5 POINTS

Baked potato

Eating a baked potato is a great way to keep warm on Bonfire Night. What's your favourite filling?

Hot dog

No one really knows how hot dogs got their name, but these sausages in buns are another Bonfire Night favourite.

61

Food and drink

Parkin

This spiced cake is traditionally made in the north of England around Bonfire Night. If you can't see it in the shops, try making some yourself.

25 POINTS

Index

i-SPY How to get your i-SPY certificate and badge

Let us know when you've become a super-spotter with 1000 points and we'll send you a special certificate and badge!

Here's what to do:

✓ Ask an adult to check your score.

✓ Apply for your certificate at www.collins.co.uk/i-SPY (if you are under the age of 13 we'll need a parent or guardian to do this).

✓ We'll email your certificate and post you a brilliant badge!